Musical The
Classics

C000200061

Hal Leonard Europe

Distributed by Music Sales

Exclusive Distributors:
Music Sales Limited
8/9 Frith Street, London W1D 3JB, England.
Music Sales Pty Limited
120 Rothschild Avenue, Rosebery, NSW 2018, Australia.

Order No. HLE90001432
ISBN 0-7119-8724-6
This book © Copyright 2001 by Hal Leonard Europe

Printed in the USA
Cover design by Chloë Alexander

CD recorded in the USA
Vocalists: Stephen Powell; Jeffrey Ray; Sam Van Ness
Pianists: Rick Walters; Sue Malmberg

Your Guarantee of Quality
As publishers, we strive to produce every book to the highest
commercial standards.
The book has been carefully designed to minimise awkward page
turns and to make playing from it a real pleasure.
Throughout, the printing and binding have been planned to ensure a
sturdy, attractive publication which should give years of enjoyment.
If your copy fails to meet our high standards, please inform us and
we will gladly replace it.

Music Sales' complete catalogue describes thousands of titles and is
available in full colour sections by subject, direct from Music Sales
Limited. Please state your areas of interest and send a cheque/postal
order for £1.50 for postage to: Music Sales Limited, Newmarket
Road, Bury St. Edmunds, Suffolk IP33 3YB, England.

www.musicsales.com

Page		Full Performance CD Track	Piano Accompaniment CD Track
4	Do I Love You Because You're Beautiful* CINDERELLA	1	11
6	If I Loved You* CAROUSEL	2	12
10	The Impossible Dream* MAN OF LA MANCHA	3	13
14	Oh, What A Beautiful Mornin'* OKLAHOMA!	4	14
26	Only With You† NINE	6	16
32	Some Enchanted Evening** SOUTH PACIFIC	7	17
21	Sorry-Grateful* COMPANY	5	15
36	Stars* LES MISERABLES	8	18
41	The Surrey With The Fringe On Top** OKLAHOMA!	9	19
50	This Nearly Was Mine* SOUTH PACIFIC	10	20

On the CD...
Vocalists: *Stephen Powell; **Jeffrey Ray; †Sam Van Ness
Pianists: Rick Walters; Sue Malmberg

Do I Love You Because You're Beautiful?

from CINDERELLA

Lyrics by OSCAR HAMMERSTEIN II
Music by RICHARD RODGERS

If I Loved You
from CAROUSEL

Lyrics by OSCAR HAMMERSTEIN II
Music by RICHARD RODGERS

Allegretto moderato

BILLY: *(speaks ad lib.)* It'd be awful. I can just see myself.

Kind - a scraw - ny and

pale, pick - in' at my food And love - sick like an - y oth - er

guy _____ I'd throw a - way my sweat - er And dress up like a

All I'd want you to know.

If I loved you, Words would-n't come in an eas - y way

'Round in cir - cles I'd go!

Long - in' to tell you, but a - fraid and shy.

The Impossible Dream

(The Quest)

from MAN OF LA MANCHA

Lyric by JOE DARION
Music by MITCH LEIGH

Not too slow (Tempo di Bolero)

12

Oh, What A Beautiful Mornin'
from OKLAHOMA!

Lyrics by OSCAR HAMMERSTEIN II
Music by RICHARD RODGERS

CURLY:

There's a

bright, gold-en haze on the mead-ow, ___ There's a bright, gold-en

haze on the mead-ow,____ The corn is as high as an el - e-phant's

eye, An' it looks like it's climb-in' clear up to the sky.

pp *a tempo* *poco rit*

Moderato

Oh, what a beau-ti-ful morn - in' Oh, what a

p *a tempo*

beau-ti-ful day____ I got a beau-ti-ful feel -

in' Ev - 'ry - thin's go - in' my way.

All the

cat - tle are stand - in' like stat - ues, _____ All the

cat - tle are stand - in' like stat - ues, _____ They

don't turn their heads as they see me ride by, But a

8va

a tempo

lit - tle brown mav -'rick is wink - in' her eye.

poco rit

Oh, what a beau - ti - ful morn - in',

p a tempo

Oh, what a beau - ti - ful day,

Sorry - Grateful

from COMPANY

Music and Lyrics by
STEPHEN SONDHEIM

You're al-ways sor - ry,__ You're al-ways grate - ful,__ You're

al-ways wond -'ring__ what might have been.__ Then she walks in.__ And

still you're sor - ry, And still you're grate - ful, And still you won - der And

In the show Harry, Larry and David alternate verses in this song.

22

Strict rhythm

drift a - way,_ And scared she'll stay._ Good things get bet-ter,

Bad get worse._ Wait, I think I meant that in re - verse._ You're

Tempo I⁰

sor - ry — grate - ful, Re - gret'-ful — hap - py. Why look for an - swers where

none oc - cur?_ You'll al - ways be_ what you al - ways were,_ Which has

Only With You
from NINE

Words and Music by
MAURY YESTON

Each verse of the song is sung to a different woman

28

Some Enchanted Evening

from SOUTH PACIFIC

Lyrics by OSCAR HAMMERSTEIN II
Music by RICHARD RODGERS

Stars
from LES MISÉRABLES

Music by CLAUDE-MICHEL SCHÖNBERG
Lyrics by HERBERT KRETZMER and ALAIN BOUBLIL

face, till we come face to face. He knows his way in the

dark, but mine is the way of the Lord. And those who fol- low the

path of the right-eous shall have their re - ward. And if they

fall as Lu - ci - fer fell, the flame, the sword!

38

aim. And each in your sea-son re-turns and re-turns and is al-ways the

same. And if you fall as Lu-ci-fer fell, you

fall ___ in flame! And so it has been, and so it is writ-ten on the

door - ways to par-a-dise,___ that those who fal-ter and those who fall ___ must

pay ____ the price. _____

Lord, let me find him, ____ that I may see him ____ safe be-hind

dim. *p*

f

bars! _____ I will nev-er rest _____ 'til then. _____ This I

swear! This I swear by the stars. _____

rall.

rall.

The Surrey With The Fringe On Top

from OKLAHOMA!

Lyrics by OSCAR HAMMERSTEIN II
Music by RICHARD RODGERS

shin-y lit-tle sur-rey with the fringe on the top!

Brightly

I would say the fringe was made of silk

Would-n't have no oth-er kind but silk

Has it real-ly got a team of snow - white hors - es? Well,

48

(gradually slower to the end)

Hush! You bird, my ba-by's a-sleep-in'— May-be got a dream worth a-keep-in'— Whoa! you team, and jist keep a-creep-in' at a slow clip clop. Don't you hur-ry with the sur-rey with the fringe on the top.

pp rit. e dim.

This Nearly Was Mine

from SOUTH PACIFIC

Lyrics by OSCAR HAMMERSTEIN II
Music by RICHARD RODGERS

Tempo di Waltz espressivo

EMILE:

One   dream   in   my   heart _____   One

par - a - dise _____ This near - ly was mine. _____

Close to my heart she came _____ On - ly to fly a-

way _____ On - ly to fly as day flies from

moon - light. _____ Now, now I'm a - lone _____

*Repeat can be started here.

Still dream-ing of par-a-dise, _____ Still

say-ing that par-a-dise _____ Once near-ly was mine. _____

Fine

So clear and deep are my fan - cies _____ Of things I

wish _____ were true _____ I'll keep re - mem - b'ring